LEGO® City Fire Chief Freya McCloud here. Build me and my robot, then we'll begin our adventure.

BLEEP BLEEP!

There's a fire at the pizza place! Find and count all the pizza boxes before they're lost forever.

PIZZA =

Who will win the junkyard race? Find out on page 29.

There's another fire on page 18. Help me put it out.

Can you find all eight of these objects in the busy scene? Circle them as you go.

ALL IN A DAY'S WORK

"Special reporter Gabby ToCamera here," says Gabby. "Today I'm joined by Fire Chief Freya McCloud to tell us all about the rescue at the fireworks factory."

"As always, things went like clockwork," says Freya. "The alarm bell rang and everyone in the team knew exactly what to do."

"As we were leaving, I told Bob and Clemmons to fetch everything we needed to get the fire under control."

"Did they manage?" asks Gabby. "Of course!" smiles Freya.

"What happened next?" asks Gabby. "My team made it to the fire in the blink of an eye, of course!" says Freya.

"I'm impressed," says Gabby. "My team is the best in the business," grins Freya.

"The LEGO City Fire Department is prepared for every situation ..."

"... and we know how to celebrate a job well done, too!" Freya adds with a wink to the camera.

Find the names of the fire team in the grid.
Names can go either up and down or side to side.

C	F	E	L	D	M	A	N
A	C	A	F	R	O	T	T
B	B	F	R	E	Y	A	M
O	E	K	Q	K	S	Z	C
B	F	B	U	S	T	E	R
E	Y	Z	M	T	S	R	B
C	L	E	M	M	O	N	S
G	K	U	R	O	L	C	D

FREYA

CLEMMONS

BOB

FELDMAN

BUSTER

Can you work out which two of these
badges are different from the others?

A   B   C

D   E   F

Fire Chief Freya's office is a little untidy. Can you find the one picture from each column below that also appears in the messy scene?

I'll tidy up just as soon as I've completed this level of my game.

Help Clemmons and Bob drive to Freya to pick her up.
Make sure they collect everything she needs on their way.

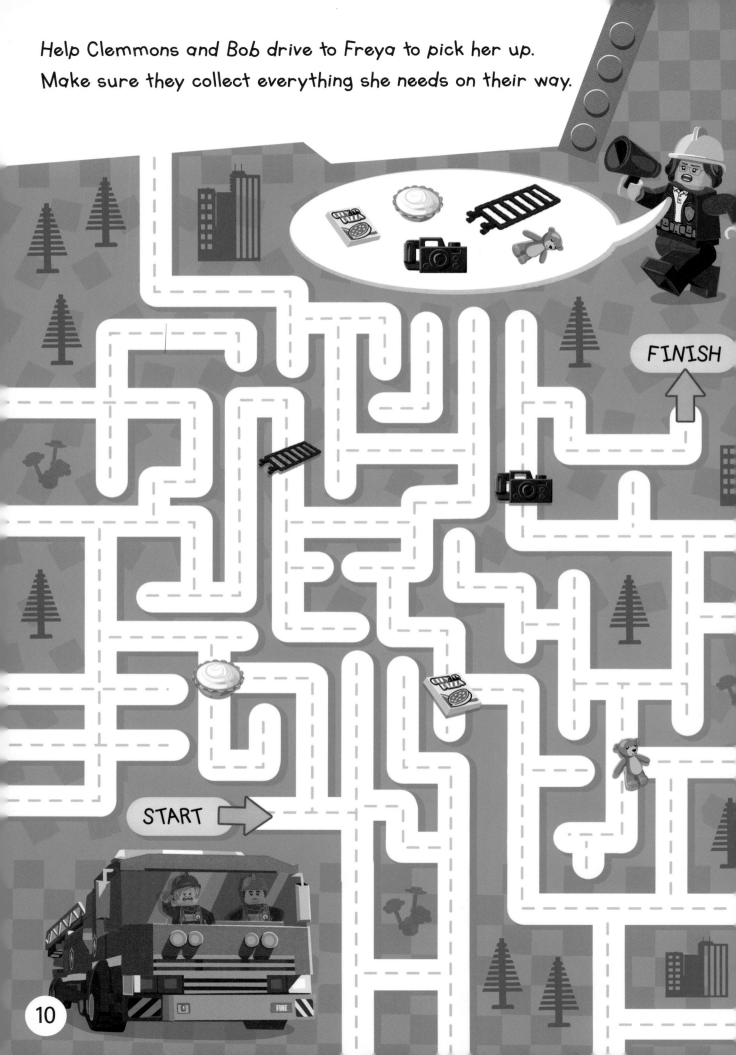

START

FINISH

Colour in the white fire extinguishers so that each colour only appears once in every row and column.

That looks tricky!

Bob is trying to match the close-ups with the fire vehicles. Can you help him?

A   B   C   D   E

The LEGO City Fire Department needs a new uniform.
Use pens, pencils or crayons to design one for them.

Buster always arrives in style. Bring him down to earth by drawing along his path without going over the lines.

Nice of you to drop in!

Which picture perfectly matches Freya's robot?

A

B

C

The Funky 46 are the funkiest firefighters around!
Join up the picture halves by colouring in their symbols
with a matching colour.

The Funky 46? I love
you guys!

Follow the tangled lines to find out which firefighter is taking which vehicle to the next rescue mission.

A

B

C

There's no time to lose!

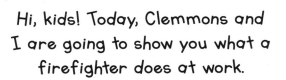

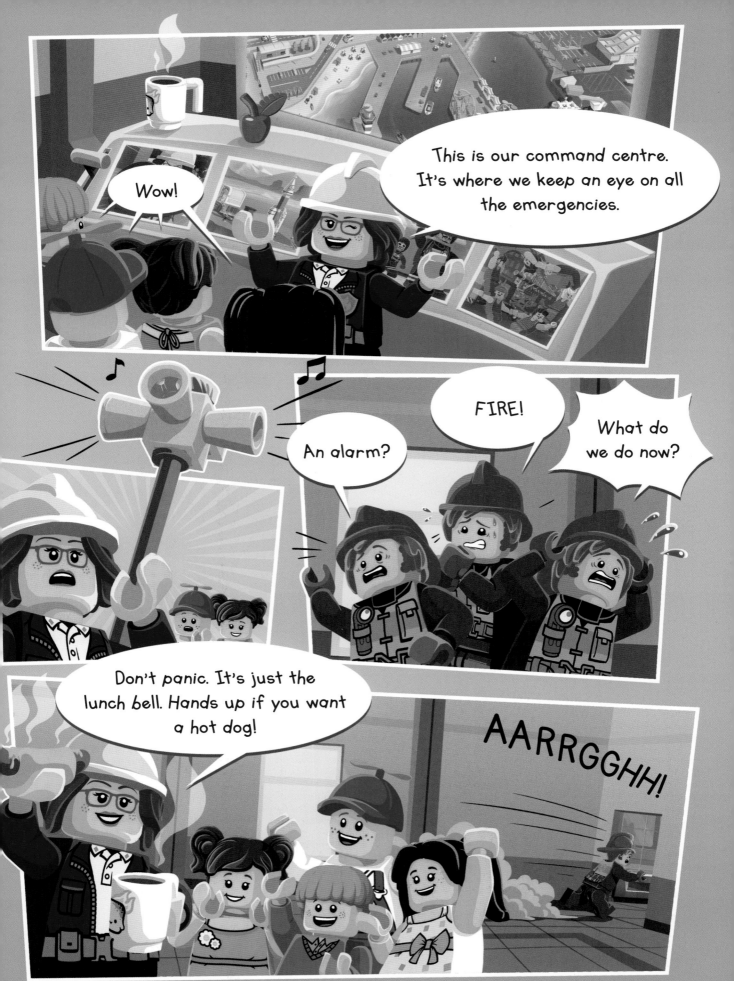

Help the crew put out this fire by completing the jigsaw.
Write the correct letters in the empty spaces.

A   B   C

D   E   F

Freya's helicopter is missing some parts. Write the correct numbers in the empty circles to put it back together.

Roastie is a firefighting robot who loves to dance! Which of Roastie's dance moves matches the silhouette?

Roastie is my best friend!

Spot the eight differences between these two pictures of the fire at the whipped cream factory. Colour in a LEGO City resident each time you find a difference.

Look at the small pictures below. Where they match what's happening above, circle 'T' for 'true'. Where they don't, circle 'F' for 'false'.

Can you find Roastie's path to Freya? Roastie can only go on squares with red hats, and can't move diagonally.

START

You can do it, Roastie!

FINISH

Which hose should be turned off to save Clemmons?

C

B

A

Buster is flying to a fire on a drone! Which of the flipped pictures is a true mirror image of the bigger picture?

A

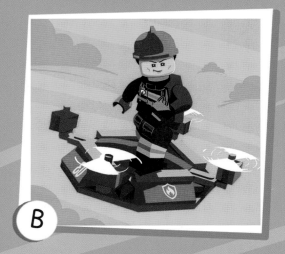

B

C

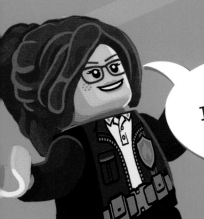

I'm impressed!

D

23

Draw the facial expressions Clemmons makes in these situations.

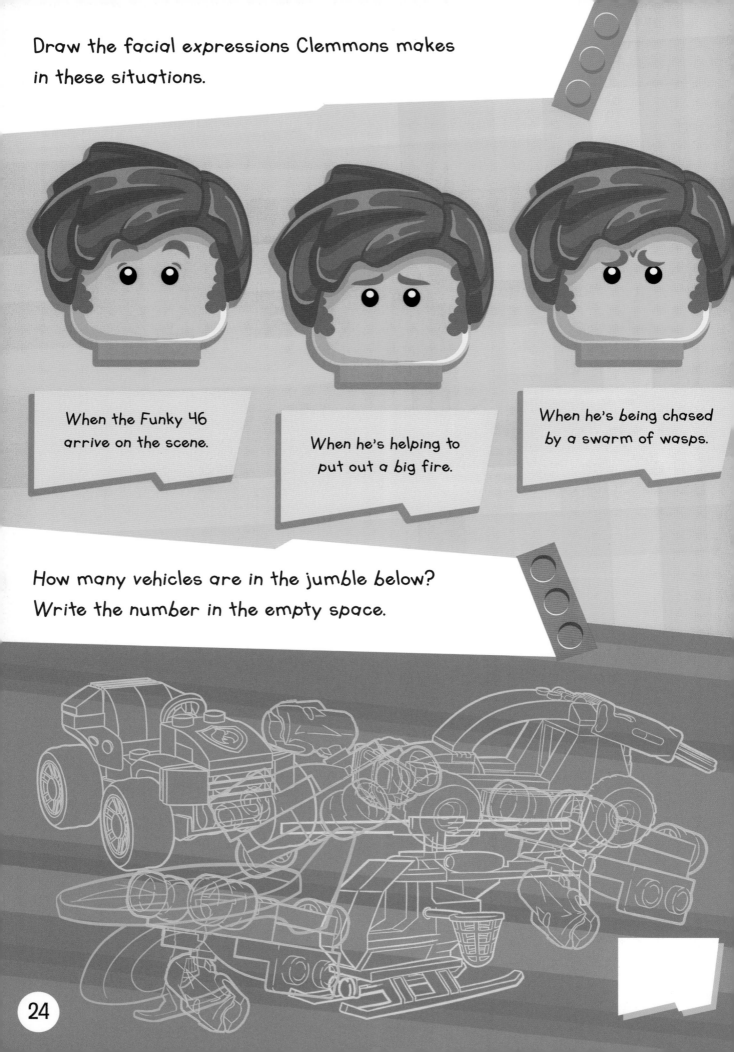

When the Funky 46 arrive on the scene.

When he's helping to put out a big fire.

When he's being chased by a swarm of wasps.

How many vehicles are in the jumble below?
Write the number in the empty space.

Bob! Clemmons! I need a teddy bear, a sheet, two palm trees and an umbrella.

But boss ...

Hurry up!

What does she need these things for?

No idea ... but it must be a real emergency.

A few moments later ...

Just in time ...

... for my nap.

Huh?

The firefighters are off to another emergency. Which path has the fewest obstacles?

The Funky 46 have the best dance moves in the whole of LEGO City. Can you spot which of their funky moves is missing from each group?

Who did Clemmons rescue from a forest fire? Use the dots as a guide to colour in the picture.

Twit-twoo to you too!

Can you spot Fire Chief Freya's favourite cocoa mug?
It's the one that is different from the others.

Now I can have a nice hot drink.

Only two of the small pictures appear in the rescue scene. Can you work out which two they are?

It's time for the big LEGO City junkyard race. Lead the racers through to find out who makes it to the finishing line.

The Funky 46   Duke DeTain   Tread Octane   Clemmons

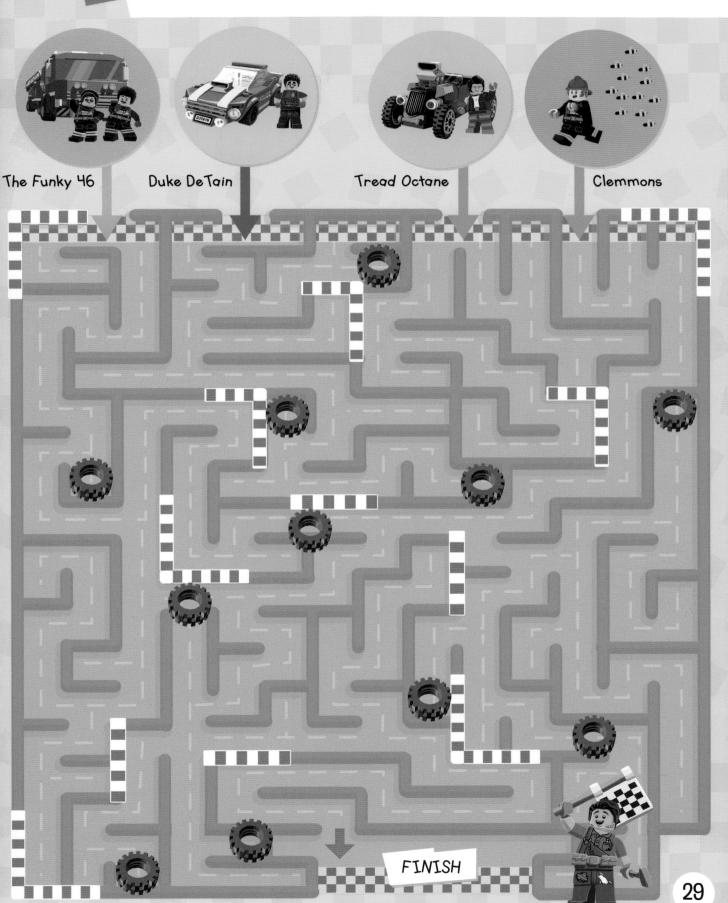

FINISH

The firefighters are taking a well-deserved break in the park. Can you draw lines to link them all to their names?

Feldman

Freya

Buster

Clemmons

Bob

The Funky 46

ANSWERS

p. 2-3

 = 6

p. 8

p. 9

p. 10

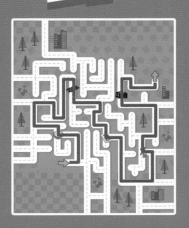

p. 11

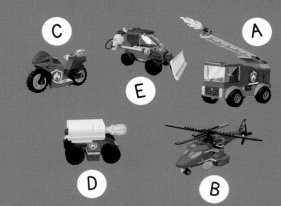

p. 11

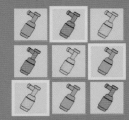

p. 13

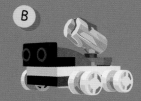

p. 14

p. 15

p. 18

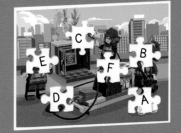

p. 19

p. 19

p. 20-21

p. 22

p. 22

p. 23

p. 24

p. 26

p. 27

p. 27

p. 28

p. 28

p. 29

p. 30